'OH NO! NOT THE '23!'

Cartoons Historical from

MIKE WILLIAMS

GRAFTON BOOKS
A Division of the Collins Publishing Group

LONDON GLASGOW
TORONTO SYDNEY AUCKLAND

To Joan, Clare and Andrea

My grateful thanks to Amanda-Jane Doran of *Punch* for her kind assistance in the preparation of this book

Grafton Books
A Division of the Collins Publishing Group
8 Grafton Street, London W1X 3LA

Published by Grafton Books 1987

British Library Cataloguing in Publication Data

Williams, Mike
Oh no! Not the '23! : cartoons historical
from Punch.
1. English wit and humor, Pictorial
I. Title
741.5'942 NC1479

ISBN 0-246-13209-4

Printed in Great Britain by
William Collins Sons & Co Ltd, Westerhill, Glasgow

Preface

I was born in 1940, a pretty significant year in the history of Europe, and that may have had some influence on my appetite for the happenings of days gone by. In fact, had I been taller, I could have waved to Adolf Hitler as he viewed us through his binoculars from the Pas-de-Calais – although, from Liverpool, it may have been stretching it a bit.

However, once Hitler had finally bunkered himself and the international dust had settled (to allow industrial pollution a chance to re-establish itself in our lives), I – after attending the now-famous Quarry Bank High School for Gentlepersons – metamorphosed into a fully fledged dogsbody in a commercial art studio in Liverpool. There I was trained in the noble arts of graphics and illustration.

I married in 1964. My wife Joan, then teaching, supported me through my early years of cartooning – my "blue period" as it became known, owing to the colourful language expressed as I waded through the rejection slips. I eventually sold my first drawing to *Punch* in the late 1960s and have been with them ever since.

Always having had a menagerie of dependent animals to look after (none of whom read history), we became used to a disproportionate amount of our limited income being swallowed up in pet food. Two daughters added to the sea of open mouths and put my sense of humour to the severest of tests.

Humour, it seems, is a decidedly human affair; animals, unfortunately, are bereft of any sense of it whatever. For instance: recently, one of our six cats, a remedial muscular Tom, leapt lightly on to the kitchen unit in his endless search for gastronomic delights and set his bottom alight on the gas flame of the adjacent cooker. My wife, who witnessed this bizarre attempt at self-immolation, instantly extinguished the flame. However – and here's the point – not once during the ensuing mêlée of hilarity and jokes ("putting the cat out") did the cat see the funny side.

So one has to conclude that the common cat (*Genus felis*), through all its stages of evolution, from the petrification of Pompeii to the introduction of the Chinese restaurant, is without a sense of humour. As with the cat, so with the rest of animalia...

Can science really be this easy? Anyway, the point I'm so nearly losing is that humour and history are left exclusively to the humanoid of the planet.

This little book is a paddle in shallow waters, with the trousers rolled slightly below the knees. The water's quite nice once you're in...

Mike Williams
February 1987

"Just think, my dear . . . if this is what man is capable of achieving in the seventeenth century, imagine what he'll be capable of by the twentieth!"

"Wow! I must paint this up when I get home."

"They must be nearly ready to sail."

"Listen, kid . . . I don't care what your mother thinks, you take it from me, with ambrosia you don't need greens."

"This is another fine mess I've got us into."

"I knew that rhino was a trouble-maker."

"Oh, for heaven's sake! I said I'll let you know!"

"Isn't life simple when you know you're right all the time!"

"I dread to think what the hotel will be like."

"And before you know, they've slammed up another of these modern monstrosities."

"Why don't you grow up, Leonardo!"

"A host? Y' call that a host? . . . why, back in the States . . ."

"...And there's the one about the Welshman and the bow-legged parrot."

"...Weather terrific, wish you were here – Robin."

"Now do we get a youth club?"

"Well, at least he won't spend half his life worrying about his silly heel."

"Run for your lives – it's the Coming of Christianity!"

"Of all the nerve! Making us sit through the whole of their Bayeux Tapestries!"

"We're out of paper."

"I said . . . Deformed! Unfinished. Sent before my time . . . into this breathing world scarce half made up. I never mentioned a word about a rise."

"To the Bastille!"

"Unaccustomed as I'll get to public speaking . . ."

"Because we're the only ones who'll remember the way back, that's why we're so bloody indispensable!"

"Aw, come off it, Christopher – the world's flat. The beer's flat and the barmaids aren't exactly overblown."

"Oh Jeremy, we can't tell you how proud we are that you're following in father's footstep."

"... well, how about your Aunt Nellie, then?"

"Aw, come on, fellas. This isn't getting the chapel painted."

"The pity is, after Goliath I'm afraid he never quite matched up to his original promise."

"Oh, not another crusade, dear!"

"I knew it! I knew it! Sooner or later I just knew there'd be a catch!"

"It's that sort of thing that gets fishing a bad name."

"It's such a nice day we've decided to stay on the beach."

". . .And that won't wake me either."

"Well, they **are** from Verona but I'm afraid that's about as far as it goes."

"Frankly, if I'd known this lot would be here I don't think I'd have bothered to come."

"A bit hyper-sensitive today, Ned?"

"Surely they don't need all those happy hunting grounds?"

"Parkinson! For Heaven's sake, man, stop or we'll all be killed!"

"You'd think if he was really that successful he'd have had his nose fixed."

"Can Sir Gilbert come out to play?"

"A pfennig *for your thoughts, Hieronymus.*"

"Just what the Hell kind of a Viking are you anyhow?"

"It's the new Inter-City, son."

"Let me through – I'm an artist!"

"Hannibal's coming!"

"Right lad, that's two Guinnesses, a lager and lime, two packets of smoky bacon and a hemlock."

"That damn'd Michelangelo kid!"

"I do love it when the decorations go up."

*"You will meet a tall dark stranger . . . Then a short dark stranger . . .
Then a medium fair stranger . . . Then a big fair stranger . . . Then a small mousey stranger . . .
Then a small dark stranger . . ."*

"Aw, come on Walter, a Government warning on every pouch isn't the end of the world."

"Great news, Your Highness! The Kennel Club's thinking of naming a spaniel after you!"

"We'd like to appeal against the light."

"Five minutes, everybody!"

"Seen enough . . . suckers?"

mike Williams.

"My God! You mean we're ***all*** *KGB?"*

Mike Williams.

"One of the really nice things about the spring is being able to turn the central heating down a little."

"Well, let's hope he gets into something soon, because let's face it, Mary, he'll never make a carpenter."

"I got sent off."

"Run! Everybody run! The little green man's starting to flash!"

"Hey!"

"I've got it! Look, he was very disappointed when he couldn't have England for last Christmas, so why don't we all get together and get him Russia for this one?"

*"That's strange, it's **exactly** like Mummy used to make."*

"Oh please! Your Highness . . . not the Glasgow Empire!"

"...and then I thought...a national hero...adulation...an international celebrity...the interminable chat shows..."

"...And if I'm really nice, he'll take me up in his helicopter."

"I made it! I made it! I'm into the quarter-finals!"

"I didn't even know he wore a contact lens."

"Relax, madam, those two have never yet got a virgin past the twenty-fourth step."

"...shark-infested custard!... Get it?...No?...
Well, never mind...how about the Irishman who...?"

"Oh boy! This is what I call Valhalla!"

"Thou canst not be serious??"

"Forty-seven! Did you hear that, Your Majesty? Sir Francis has beaten the old record by a clear ten ferrets!"

"Great . . . lovely . . . now how about one of just the two of you loading the revolver?"

"Hey, Dad! I got a girl into trouble!"

". . . And you can bet your life the architect lives in a nice little villa in the country."

“...the Sphere of
Divine Self Begetting
and a Creation...
you wanna matt
or gloss?”

“How about a whip-round
for the driver?”

*"At least we've proved one thing pretty conclusively . . .
the Polynesians are a race of raving lunatics!"*

NO SMOKING
SIR WALTER RALEIGH

TESCO
Mike Williams.

"Well, that's musketeers for you."

"Sung . . . T'ang . . . Ming . . . So who cares? You still have to dry the bloody things."

*"Gott in Himmel! **Somebody** must have a franc!"*

"It's Robin Day with 'The World at One'."

"If this is declining, then it sure beats progress."

"Wait, we may just have landed at a significant moment in this planet's evolution."

"Well, so much for Plan 'A'."

"When I was a lad we had to make our own entertainment."

"I am Igsprx from the planet Thynog – take me to your toilet."

"Personally, I blame it all on Le Corbusier."